W9-CED-307

Let's Play Tag!

Read the Page

Read the Story

Game

Sound it/Say it

Repeat

Stop

Get-Ready Words

animal	palace
chores	Prince
Duke	slipper
Fairy Godmother	Stepmother
	wand
midnight	

Cinderella

The Heart That Believes

Cinderella was sweet.
Her animal friends loved her.

Cinderella's stepmother and stepsisters were not sweet.

They made Cinderella do all the chores. They did not help.

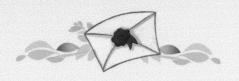

One day, the King sent a note.
There was going to be a royal ball!

The Stepmother said, "Cinderella, you
may go, *if* you get all your work done."

Then she gave Cinderella even
more chores.

 While Cinderella worked,
the animals mended her dress.

It was very pretty, but her
stepsisters tore the dress
into shreds.

 Cinderella was sad. She wanted to go to the ball.

Then her Fairy Godmother appeared!

"Now, what in the world did I do with that magic wand?" she said. "Ah! I remember."

The Fairy Godmother gave her wand a wave ...

... and Cinderella had everything she needed to go to the ball! She had a pretty dress and glass slippers, too.

"You'll have only until midnight," the Fairy Godmother told Cinderella.

 Cinderella rode to the palace.

She met the Prince at the ball.

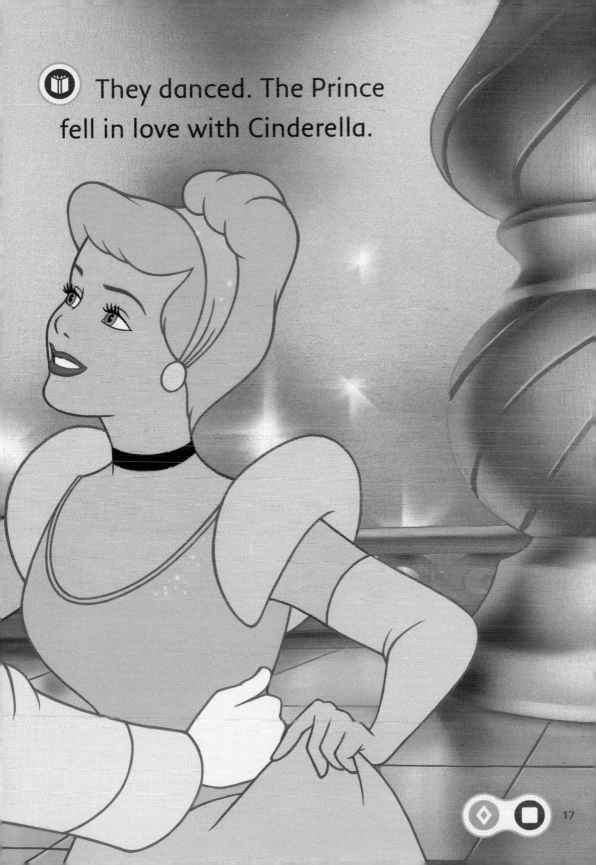

They danced. The Prince
fell in love with Cinderella.

 Cinderella had a
wonderful time. She did
not know how late it was.

Then she heard the clock.

"Oh my goodness! It's
midnight!" she said.
"I must leave."

Cinderella ran. She lost
a slipper.

The King sent the Grand Duke to every home. He needed to find the maiden who had lost the slipper. The Prince wanted to ask that girl to marry him. The Grand Duke went to Cinderella's home.

The Stepmother locked Cinderella in her room.

Cinderella's stepsisters tried on the slipper. It did not fit.

The mice took the key to Cinderella's room. They let Cinderella out.

Cinderella tried on the slipper. It fit!

Cinderella and the Prince lived happily ever after.

The End

Words You're Learning

Short Vowels

Short a Words	Short e Words	Short i Words	Short o Words	Short u Words
and	dress	fit	clock	but
grand	fell	him	lost	must
had	help	if	not	
ran	let	slipper	on	
sad	sent			

Long Vowels

Long a Words	Long e Words	Long i Words	Long o Words	Long u/oo Words
day	key	mice	home	duke
gave	leave	time	know	room
late	sweet	while	note	too
made			rode	who
may				

Sight Words

all	my	the	what
do	one	there	with
go	she	to	you